A play by Chris Buckton

LIGHT THE BEACONS

Illustrations by Mike Spoor

CHARACTERS

Narrator
Matthew as an old man.
He is an old sailor
thinking about the past.
He speaks slowly and
thoughtfully.

Bess Prior, aged 11
She is the eldest of the
Prior children. She's
quiet and sensible. She
understands Matthew's
feelings.

Matthew Prior, aged 9
He has very strong
feelings. He wants to be
a hero and doesn't like
being told what to do.

Hal Prior, aged 6
He is excited about the
war and always curious
about everything. He has
a pet dog called Mop.

Thomas Prior
He is the children's father and village watchman. He is worried about the war. He is a very responsible person.

Anne Prior
She is the children's mother. She can be quite bossy but she's got a kind heart.

Sound effects
Door
Pots and pans
Wind whistling
Distant drums and shouting
Dog barking
Flint being struck (scraping sound)
Fire (crumpling paper)
Church bells (chime bar)

3

Time: July/August 1588

Setting: a village on the south coast of England near Plymouth

PROLOGUE

Narrator *(Matthew as an old man)* When I was a lad I longed for adventure. I had dreams, just like all children since the world began.

Most of all, I dreamed of being a sailor and fighting for Admiral Drake. He was my hero.

Our family lived near Plymouth. The year that I was nine, we were all afraid that the Spanish Armada would attack us. The ships in Plymouth harbour were getting ready to defend England. I yearned to join the navy. Sometimes they would enlist boys if they were tall enough…

Scene One

The Priors' cottage on 30 July, early morning. Anne,
Thomas, Bess and Hal are at breakfast.

Thomas *(worried)* They say in the village
that it can't be long now. We
must pray to be safeguarded
from our enemies.

Anne *(anxiously)* The preacher says that
our enemies will torture us. I fear
for our children. I fear for ourselves.

Hal *(not really scared, he thinks it's all a
game)* What will they do to us?
Will they put us in a dungeon?

Bess Our ships will defeat the Spanish!
Drake set their ships afire last year!

Thomas But our ships are small. Our sailors
may be brave but the Spanish
outnumber us. Their galleons
with their great sails will sweep
us up like crumbs on their table.

Anne Let's have no more of that dangerous talk. Hal, go and bid your brother rise for his breakfast. Is he going to lie a-bed all day? There's work to be done.

Hal runs off. Bess looks guilty and starts to speak.

Bess Mother, I –

Hal *(shouting)* Matthew isn't here! His bed's empty!

He comes clattering back downstairs and sits at the table.

Bess Mother, don't be afraid. He's safe enough. I know where he is.

Anne Well, tell us girl, tell us at once.

Bess He's gone down to the harbour. He's intent on joining the navy.

Thomas *(laughing)* The boy's a lunatic! He's but a child! They won't consider him!

Bess *(fiercely)* Don't mock him! Did you not have dreams when you were a boy? He wants to play his part.

She is interrupted by the door opening. Matthew comes in, head hanging, looking miserable. He sits down at the table.

Hal   *(excited)* Did they take you, Matt?
              (Bess kicks him) Ouch!

Anne   *(gently)* Eat your porridge now,
              Matthew. You're just a boy. Be patient.

Matthew   *(beginning to cry)* But the danger is here
              now! I want to help. I want to fight.

A tear drops into his porridge.

Thomas   If you want to help, then come up
              the hillside and stack logs with me.
              I must be ready to light the beacon
              as soon as the Armada is sighted.
              The fire will be a signal to our
              soldiers. They will defend us if the
              Spanish land on our shores.

Matthew   *(scornfully)* Lighting the beacon isn't
              real war.

Hal   *(excited)* It is, it is! Father is
              watchman, he'll send the signal!
              Can I help too?

Thomas I would be glad of you all today.

Anne *(worried)* You're not well, Thomas, you're shivering. You have a fever coming. Can you not ask neighbour William to take your watch?

Thomas *(firmly)* No, I must do my duty. I must keep the watch.

Scene Two

The hillside that afternoon. Wind blowing, larks singing. Matthew, Bess, Hal and their father are stacking wood at the top of the hill. There is a big iron fire basket on a post. Next to it is a little wooden hut. Thomas is coughing.

Thomas As soon as they spy the Spanish ships, they'll light the beacon on the Plymouth hill. And that fire will be the signal for me to light this beacon.

Bess And then the next village will see it and light theirs…

Hal And then the next…

Matthew And the next, all the way to London and the Queen!

Thomas That's right. The chain mustn't be broken.

Bess So the whole of England will know that the Armada is come. And the soldiers will come to defend us.

Hal But how will you light the fire quickly enough?

Thomas See here, I keep some dry tinder in this pocket. And my flint in its little box. I've laid the wood all ready in the iron basket. I'll need a steady hand.

Hal What if it rains?

Thomas Here's my hut for shelter. And I have some dry logs inside.

Hal   There's no seat for you to rest on. You'll get tired.

Thomas   There's no seat, lad, lest I should fall asleep. I must watch every moment.

They look down towards Plymouth.

Bess   I can see the harbour … and there's the Plymouth beacon ready to be lit.

Hal   What if the Spanish land in Plymouth? Are the soldiers ready?

Matthew   Drake wants to fight the Spanish at sea, and stop them from landing. That's right, Father, isn't it?

Thomas   Yes, son. The army will do their best, but they're not strong. They're not well trained. Better to fight the battles at sea.

Matthew   And we have better sailors than the Spanish.

Bess   And Drake can do anything. He raided the ships in Cadiz harbour and singed the King of Spain's beard!

Hal   But, Father, you said the English ships are small, next to the great Spanish galleons.

Thomas   Maybe small ships will be faster. *(Wearily, coughing, shivering)* We must place our trust in God.

Bess   *(anxiously)* You're not well, Father … and it's a lonely job.

Thomas   I must keep watch. And you must help your mother while I'm away up here on the hillside. Go back now. And bring me my supper tonight.

The children run off down the hillside, waving and calling goodbye as they go.

Scene Three

The hillside on the same night. Strong wind blowing. The children are scrambling through the bracken, climbing the hill breathlessly. They are carrying their father's supper in a basket covered with a cloth.

Hal   Do you think Father's afraid, up here alone in the dark?

Matthew   *(scornfully)* I wouldn't be afraid.

Bess   He'll be glad of warm broth and bread.

They reach the top – but there's no sign of Thomas.

Hal   Where is he? Why isn't he watching?

Bess   Something must have happened.

Matthew   Look! Over there! Father is lying by the wood pile!

Bess   He's sick. Sick with fever. We must cover him with our cloaks. We must keep him warm.

The children take their cloaks off and tuck them round their father.

Bess Can you hear me, Father? We're here, we'll get help.

Thomas *(weakly)* Watch hard for smoke ... Look towards Plymouth ... Keep your eyes ...

Hal *(crying)* Father! Wake up! I'm frightened. We must get help.

Matthew *(urgently)* But we must keep watch as well. The chain mustn't be broken!

Bess Hal, could you be brave enough to run back to the cottage and raise the alarm? Matthew and I must stay on watch.

Hal Do you know how to light the tinder?

Matthew I know how to strike the flint.

Bess Let's pray that help will come before we need to.

Hal I'll go like the wind.

Matthew Then run, Hal!

Hal runs off.

Matthew Keep your eyes fixed on Plymouth. I'll find Father's tinder and flint.

He searches Thomas's pockets and finds them. Thomas groans but doesn't speak.

Matthew Father is burning hot. What if he should …

Bess *(briskly)* We mustn't think about it. Hal will get help. We must just watch.

Bess and Matthew keep their eyes fixed on Plymouth.

Matthew *(teeth chattering)* Can you see the harbour lights? My eyes are aching from staring into the darkness.

Bess Let's sing to keep our spirits up.

She starts to hum a tune.

Matthew *(quietly)* I said I wouldn't be afraid but it's so dark. I'm glad you're here too, Bess.

Bess *(excited)* Look, Matthew – what's that? Is it smoke rising up? Is it? Can it be?

Sounds of drums and shouting in the distance.

Matthew Listen! Drums!

Bess And shouting! Yes, the Plymouth beacon is blazing!

Matthew The Armada is come! *(Shivering)* Oh Bess, I'm afraid to do this alone. What if I can't light the beacon? What if we fail?

Bess Think how we strike the flint for the fire at home. We won't fail.

Matthew I can feel my heart like a hammer.

Bess My hand is shaking. But we won't fail.

Sounds of flint being struck.

Bess Look! A spark is catching! Put on more tinder!

Rustling sounds. Then a pause.

15

Matthew	*(desperately)* Oh no! The spark's gone out!
Bess	*(urgently)* Try again! Quick, we only have a little tinder left.

Sound of flint again. The children hold their breath.

Bess	*(whispering)* There's a spark!
Matthew	The wind is too strong. I'll shield the fire with my jerkin.

He takes off his jerkin and holds it in front of the fire.

Matthew	*(hopefully)* The spark is still alight! It's glowing … and growing!

Sound of fire burning.

Bess I can hear it crackling!

Matthew *(excited)* It's alight! We've done it!
Quick, Bess, more wood!

Bess The smoke is streaming in the
wind. We've done it!

The children cheer and whoop in excitement.

Thomas *(stirring, muttering)* Don't break
the chain!

Scene Four

*The Priors's cottage the following day. Thomas is safely in
bed. The children are clustered round. Anne comes in
carrying a hot drink.*

Anne *(scolding)* Now lie still, Thomas,
and drink this hot posset. I've
picked herbs from the garden to
make you well again.

Thomas *(weakly)* How good it is to be safe
at home. Last night was like a
dark dream. I just remember the
world seeming to turn round …

Hal You had fainted, Father. We
found you lying on the ground.

Bess And Hal here was so brave, he ran
back alone and fetched neighbour
William. William carried you on
his back.

Thomas *(proudly)* You were all brave. Bess, you were as brave as Good Queen Bess herself. And Hal, like her father King Henry. *(He stops to cough)*

Matthew *(eagerly)* What about me, Father?

Thomas *(laughing)* I said you were nothing but a child, and you said that lighting the beacon wasn't real war.

Matthew I know better now.

Thomas Aye, and so do I. You did a man's job. Drake himself would be proud to have you as a son.

Bess *(proudly)* The chain wasn't broken.

Anne They say in the market that the beacons burned all night. The fires blazed all along the south coast.

Matthew Father, our ships sailed out of the harbour. They're lying in wait, and the wind has driven the Armada up the channel.

Thomas We'll pluck their feathers little by little. But it won't be done for many a year. One day, my boy, maybe one day you'll be at Drake's side …

EPILOGUE

Sounds of church bells pealing.

Narrator I'll never forget the church bells and
the cheering when the Armada was
defeated, and their ships driven north
by the storms. All those great
galleons wrecked on the rocks.

And one thing I keep by me always.

Gets a medal out of his pocket, holds it lovingly.

A medal to remind us of that victory. I
know its words by heart: "God
blew and they were scattered".

It wasn't the end of the war, though.
My father was right. When I was
fourteen I joined the navy and sailed
with Drake against the Spanish.

But that night was the start of it all –
the night I lit the beacon. That was
the beginning of the real war for me.

Church bells sound again.

TIMELINE

April 1587 Admiral Drake "singes the King of Spain's beard" in Cadiz.

May 1588 Armada sails from Lisbon.

22 July English fleet anchors in Plymouth.

30 July Sea captain tells Drake that the Armada is sighted in Plymouth Sound.

30 July Beacons lit.

31 July Wind drives Spanish up the Channel with the English behind them. Battle near Plymouth.

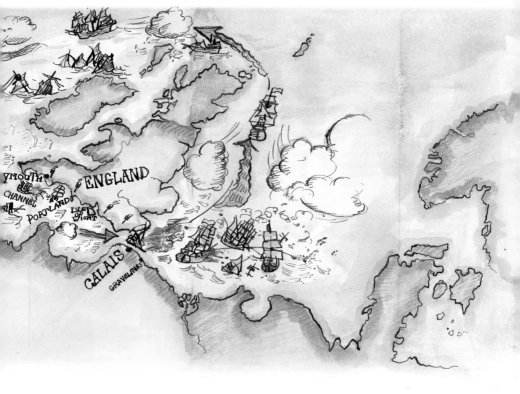

1–2 August Battle near Portland Bill.

3–4 August Battle near Isle of Wight.

7 August Spanish anchor at Calais. English send fireships into Calais harbour.

8 August Battle of Gravelines.

21 August Spanish ships driven north by storms.

26 October Last ship of Armada sinks off Irish coast.

1596 Death of Drake.

1603 Death of Queen Elizabeth I.

READY, STEADY, ACT!

Now that you have read this play it's time to act it out. You will tell your audience the story using words, actions and maybe some costumes and props.

CHOOSING THE PARTS

Choose who will play each part.

- The narrator could read his part. He should sound as if he is remembering.
- Matthew is lively and excitable, and will have to act many emotions.
- Bess is a steady girl who looks after her brothers.
- Hal is a happy child, too young to understand how serious the war is.
- Thomas, their father, will need to act being ill convincingly.
- Anne, their mother, is really proud of her family and orders them about.

Make name stickers for your characters to wear.

> Did you know…?
> Did you know that Drake 'singed the King of Spain's beard' by sailing into Cadiz harbour, burning 31 ships, capturing six more, and setting back Spain's invasion plans by up to a year?

SETTING THE SCENE

The action takes place in the family cottage and on the hillside during the day and then at night.
A table and chairs for the breakfast scene will show that you are inside. Can you use a different acting space for the hillside?

WHAT YOU WILL NEED

Costumes

Keep it simple! Use long skirts for girls, trousers tucked into socks for boys, hats, and waistcoats. When they go out to the hillside, they will need to be wrapped in cloaks or blankets.

Props

Make a props list from the script and decide which you can find or make. The hardest thing will be the iron fire basket. How about wrapping a bin in paper and painting it to look like a basket. It will need to be high up, so fix it securely.

Special effects

Your night scene will be more dramatic if you can play it in the dark with just a spotlight. Perhaps someone could carry a lantern.

SPEAKING AND MOVING

Speaking

This play has many tense moments. Choose some dialogue and practise how you will deliver the lines to make the audience feel tense too. Can you make the tension rise as the children try to light the beacon?

Moving

How will you

- show the children running down the hill?
- show how Father moves as he gets sicker?
- show 'scrambling through the bracken'?

What next?

When you have performed this play, you might want to:

- Do some research about Sir Francis Drake's piratical activities
- Look at an atlas and plot the route of the Armada.